Breakfast with Ublob

Sam McBratney

Illustrated by
Nick Schon

Series Editors
Steve Barlow and Steve Skidmore

Breakfast with Ublob

Do you have trouble with your dilix pumps? Have you ever heard of square cold water? Neither had Edward and Helen until a visitor from space landed in their back garden. His name was Ublob.

Edward and Helen were delighted with their visitor from the Milky Way, and so were their mum and dad. However, they found that when it came to giving Ublob some breakfast, he was rather hard to please...

The Main Characters

Edward
Edward is the first person to talk to Ublob after he lands in the garden. He is very interested in Ublob, especially in his ideas about food.

Helen
Helen is Edward's younger sister. She is very curious about Ublob, too. It is Helen who finally solves the problem of the square cold water.

Ublob
Ublob comes from the Milky Way, and everything on Earth seems strange to him, including Edward and Helen. Ublob should look as strange as possible, and his voice should sound flat, like a machine.

Mum
Mum does her best to give Ublob a good breakfast, but it isn't easy.

Other characters in the play are Helen and Edward's **father** and **three children** from nearby. These characters don't have very much to say.

Scene 1

(Helen and Edward are playing in their garden before they go to school in the morning. Edward is juggling with three apples. Suddenly Helen looks up and frowns.)

Helen: Edward, I can hear something.

Edward: Don't talk to me when I'm trying to juggle. You put me off.

Helen: But I can hear something. It sounds like a helicopter and it's coming closer. Look!

(They both look up.)

Edward: That's not a helicopter. It's coming down to land in our garden.

Helen: Come on, let's hide behind the coal bunker.

(Helen and Edward hide as the spacecraft lands out of sight of the audience.)

Edward: What is that thing? Do you think there's anybody inside it?

Helen: I don't know. There can't be much room in there, it's not much bigger than our garden shed. I can see a door.

Edward: And it's opening. Who is *that?*

(Ublob walks forward, watched by the two children behind the coal bunker. Ublob stands in front of the wheely-bin.)

Ublob: Bleeben uben nynigan faroonder?

5

Edward: *(Whispering)* He's talking to the wheely-bin!

(Ublob shakes his head and moves on.)

Ublob: Vil dee minvergloben misty von hi?

Helen: Edward, he's trying to talk to the whirligig *clothesline.*

(Edward stands up and walks forward.)

Edward: That's only a clothesline. It doesn't say much.

(Ublob bows, and fiddles with the knobs of his backpack.)

Ublob: Barkon fry nur spriggling darkly. Excuse me please. I must adjust my language translator. Ink fan doh. *(After a pause)* Thank you. Good early morning. My name is Ublob and I come from Planet Ix.

Helen: Hi.

Edward: My name is Edward and you are the funniest looking person I have ever seen.

Ublob: Thank you. Where is this, please?

Helen: England.

Ublob: This is the Planet England?

Edward: No, England isn't a planet – the planet is called Earth.

Ublob: And does everyone on Earth look the same as you?

Edward: I suppose so. Some of them are a bit bigger than me, that's all. And some of them are girls. *(Points at Helen)* She's a girl.

(Helen waggles her fingers at Ublob, who bows.)

Helen: Are you on your holidays or something?

Ublob: I am returning to Planet Ix. However, my spaceship has developed a problem. I need nay naak queely fasser for my dilix pumps. Have you such a thing?

Edward: Nay naak queely fasser?

Ublob: Yes. My translator says this means ... (*He fiddles with his backpack*) ... square cold water.

Helen: I don't think we've got any. We don't have square water on Earth.

Edward: Where is Planet Ix, anyway?

Ublob: It is in the Milky Way, far beyond your Sun. I may never get back there unless I can repair my spacecraft. (*With concern*) This is a terrible emergency.

Mum: (*Offstage*) Come on you two, it's time to get ready for school.

Edward: Let's talk to Mum and Dad – they might know what to do. (*As they walk off*) Mum, we've got a visitor. He's from the Milky Way and he wants to know have we any square cold water for his thingumybob ...

Scene 2

(Edward, Helen, Mum and Dad, and Ublob are sitting in the kitchen. Dad is ready to leave for work. They are all thinking hard.)

Dad: Let's see ... There's fresh water, running water. Distilled water ...

Edward: And salt water.

Helen: And boiling water ...

Mum: There's even spring water. And rain water. But I've never heard of square water before.

Ublob: Square *cold* water. It must be cold.

Dad: And you say you'll be stuck here if you don't get it?

Ublob: The problem is that if my dilix pumps fail, I cannot recycle oxygen in my spacecraft.

Dad: *(Rising)* Well, I must go. *(To Ublob)* Don't you worry, old chap, I'll ask some people at work about this. We've got some very clever people there and I'm sure they'll have some idea how to help. Goodbye for now.

Ublob: *(With a bow)* Thank you. Goodbye.

Dad: *(Exits, muttering)* Square water, eh? *Square* ...

(Helen bounces over to Ublob with a photograph album.)

Helen: Would you like to see some photographs of me at the beach? See – I'm learning to swim in that picture.

Edward: That's me on a rubber ring.

Ublob: Thank you. That is very interesting.

Helen: Do you have rubber rings on Planet Ix?

Ublob: We do not have any rubber rings on Planet Ix, and we do not have any sea in which to swim.

Edward: I wouldn't fancy that much. Where do you go for your holidays?

Ublob: We go to a very nice hotel in space. *(Reaching into his backpack)* I have some pictures here.

(Mum, Edward and Helen gather round.)

Helen: Is that your family? They look exactly like you, only smaller.

Mum: Here's another one. Oh look, aren't they sweet?

Edward: What's that round thing like a balloon?

Ublob: It's an air bubble. They are very expensive to hire.

Helen: Imagine floating about in a bubble! I'd love that. Don't they bash into one another and burst?

Ublob: They are very tough and very strong.

Mum: Now listen everybody, it's time for breakfast or you'll never get to school today. Edward, show Ublob into the dining-room and set the table for him, please. We can't solve the problem of square water on an empty stomach, *that's* for sure.

(Edward sets the table. Ublob sniffs at his knife and fork. The kitchen and dining-room can be on stage together with a screen between them, or you can simply pretend that the screen is there.)

Ublob: This is very interesting food you have, Edward.

Edward: That's not food, that's your knife and fork.

Ublob: Ah. My knife and fork.

Edward: Hang on, I'll get you some food. (*He goes into the kitchen.*) Better hurry up, Mum, Ublob almost ate his knife and fork.

Mum: Don't be silly, Edward, take him that bowl of cornflakes.

(*Edward goes in with the cornflakes.*)

Edward: There you are, Ublob, try some cornflakes. We eat 'em with cold milk. (*As Ublob sniffs at the cornflakes*) Is there something wrong with them?

Ublob: Your food is very different from mine. I can only eat food that does not come from plants. Could you get me some? Thank you.

Edward: You want food that doesn't come from plants? Sure, no problem.

(Edward goes into the kitchen.)

Edward: He's a fussy eater, Mum, can't take cornflakes. Anything from plants is out.

Helen: I'll bring him some toast.

Mum: You needn't bring him toast – bread comes from plants. If he won't eat cornflakes he certainly won't eat toast. Here – he can have Edward's boiled egg.

(Helen and Edward bring in the egg. Ublob sniffs and nibbles at the shell.)

Helen: You're eating the wrong bit, Ublob – that's the shell! Try the soft bit.

Ublob: I'm afraid this won't do, Helen.

Helen: Why not? An egg isn't a plant, it comes out of a hen.

Edward: And a hen is an animal.

Ublob: These hens must live on seeds and things. It is clear to me that their food comes from plants, and so I cannot eat it. Thank you.

Helen: Don't mention it.

Edward: We'll get you something else.

(They go into the kitchen.)

Edward: Hens live on plants, Mum, eggs are out. For a minute I thought he was going to eat the shell.

Mum: Dear me, he *is* a fussy one. *(She opens a cupboard.)* Now let's see what I've got that doesn't come from plants. I've got vegetable soup, but that's no good, is it? And raspberry jam – but raspberries grow on canes.

Helen: What about honey?

Mum: Well, I suppose we could try it. See what he thinks about honey.

(Helen and Edward go in with the honey.)

Helen: You'll like this lovely stuff, Ublob, it's made by bees.

Ublob: *(Sniffing)* It smells sweet.

Edward: I know, that's why we like it. Watch it doesn't make you all sticky.

Ublob: These bees you speak of – I think they get their honey from flowers, yes?

Helen: Yes, they collect nectar and take it back to the hive and make honey. It's like magic.

Ublob: But flowers are plants, are they not? This will not do, Helen, thank you.

(Edward and Helen go back to the kitchen.)

Edward: No bees on Planet Ix, Mum, honey is out.

Mum: Well, he's very hard to please, isn't he? He won't eat plants and he won't eat anything that comes from plants. I'd rather keep him a week than a fortnight!

Helen: What about cheese?

Mum: Cheese comes from cows' milk.

Edward: And cows eat grass. Why don't we try a big juicy hamburger?

Mum: Because big juicy hamburgers come from cattle, too. And we can't give him bacon because pigs eat everything, including plants.

Edward: I've got an idea. Where's my lunchbox?

(Edward takes a Mars Bar out of his lunchbox.)

Edward: He'll eat this for sure.

Mum: Somehow I don't think so.

19

Helen: Everybody likes chocolate, Mum. Come on, let's bring it to him.

(They take the Mars Bar in on a plate.)

Edward: You're going to like this, Ublob. It's called a Mars Bar.

Ublob: Thank you. How interesting. I have been to Mars but there was no one there. *(Sniffs.)*

Helen: What's wrong? It's only chocolate.

Ublob: This chocolate is not good for me. I think it must grow on trees.

Edward: Mars Bars don't grow on trees.

Helen: I wish they did.

Ublob: I find I cannot eat this food. Thank you.

(Edward and Helen go back to the kitchen.)

Edward: He can't eat chocolate, Mum, it makes his tummy funny.

Mum: His tummy is funny enough already if you ask me. What shall we do? All our food seems to come from plants in one way or another. Planet Ix must be a strange place, that's all I can say.

Helen: Let's give him something to drink.

(Edward and Helen begin to empty the cupboard.)

21

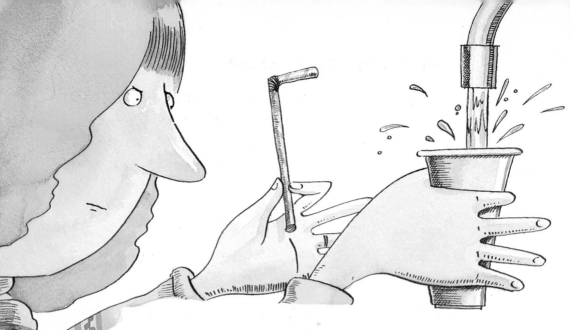

Edward: Ribena?

Mum: *(Shaking her head)* It comes from blackcurrants.

Helen: Orange juice! Oh no – oranges won't do.

Mum: Exactly. They're fruit.

Edward: So is grape juice.

Helen: He might drink tea or coffee.

Mum: Tea is leaves and coffee is beans. They grow!

Helen: How about ice-cream?

Mum: I don't think so. Right! Let's see what Mr Ublob thinks of plain old ordinary water.

(She fills a plastic cup with water and pops in a straw.)

Helen: Water? For breakfast?

Mum: There's nothing else we can give him. All the food we eat on Earth depends on plants. This water might not be *square* water – but it will have to do. Shall we go?

(Edward and Mum bring the drink to Ublob, who stands and bows.)

Mum: There you are, Ublob, we thought you might like a drink of water.

Ublob: Thank you. I am feeling quite thirsty.

(He drinks, then sniffs the cup and examines the straw. Ublob eats the straw.)

Edward: He's eating the straw!

Mum: He must think it's spaghetti.

Edward: He's eating the *cup!*

(Ublob eats the cup.)

Ublob: You have very interesting food on Planet Earth. What is it called?

Mum: It's called cup and straw, Ublob.

Ublob: *(Nodding)* Cup and straw. Interesting.

(There is a cry from Helen off-stage)

Helen: I've got it, I've got it! Square cold water – I know what it is!

(She rushes on stage waving an ice-cube tray.)

Helen: I know what it is! I thought he might like some ice-cream and then I saw them. They were in the fridge all the time!

Edward: You saw what?

Helen: Square cold water. It's ice-cubes!

(Ublob takes the tray of ice-cubes and examines it.)

Ublob: This is most wonderful. They are exactly what I have need of.

Edward: Well why didn't you say 'ice-cubes' in the first place?

Ublob: The word is not in my translator, obviously. And now, after saying thank you, I must be off. Thank you.

Mum: Will you ever come back again, Ublob?

Ublob: I will. And I must remember to ask for cup and straw the next time I am here. Would you like to see inside my spacecraft, Edward and Helen?

Edward: I would!

Helen: Me too. It's a pity you couldn't give us a lift to school.

Mum: *(As they all go off)* Don't be ridiculous, Helen, I can just see your poor teacher's face if you arrive in a space ship.

Scene 3

(A little later, in the back garden. Ublob's engines are running. Edward, Helen and Mum are there to see him off. Some children have also stopped to watch.)

First child: He's very thin-looking, isn't he? My baby sister draws people like that.

Second child: That's because he's a Martian. Martians are all thin like that.

First child:	How do you know?
Second child:	I read all about Mars in my encyclopedia. There's not much air so the people have to be thin.
Third child:	Look, he's going. He's waving goodbye.
	(All wave and shout goodbye.)
Helen:	Bye-bye, Ublob.
Ublob:	Earth is very interesting. Earth is very green. We do not have the colour green on my planet. Someday you must visit me on Planet Ix. You will like it there.
	(Ublob takes off.)

Mum: Well, there he goes. Do you know what I think, Edward?

Edward: What?

Mum: If you ever go to Planet Ix, I think you'd better take a packed lunch.

Teachers' Notes

Choosing Parts
The parts of Edward, Helen, Ublob and Mum should be read by confident readers. The parts of Dad and the First, Second and Third Children are not so demanding.

Putting On the Play
You may wish to put on a performance of the play, rather than just reading it. The following notes are suggestions which may provide you with a starting point for your own ideas about staging a production. Obviously, the use you make of these suggestions will depend on the time and resources available to your school.

For permission to put on a profit-making performance of *Breakfast with Ublob*, please contact the Editorial Department, Ginn and Company Ltd, Prebendal House, Parson's Fee, Aylesbury, Bucks HP20 2QZ.
(There is no need to apply for permission if you are not charging an entrance fee, but please let us know if you are putting on any performance of this play, as we would be interested to hear about it.)

Staging
There are three scenes in the play.
Scene 1 takes place in the garden, and has Ublob stepping out of a spacecraft. The spacecraft could be created offstage by use of dry ice or a smoke machine and stage lights. Alternatively, depending on resources available, a spacecraft could be represented on stage using cardboard boxes etc. You could also have a wheely-bin and a whirligig clothesline for this scene, or you could simply rely on the audience to imagine these!
Scene 2 takes place in the kitchen and dining room. These can be represented using a table, chairs and a work top. More elaborate designs could include kitchen utensils, models of a fridge and cooker made from boxes, and so on. There is no real need to separate the two rooms physically; they could just be on opposite sides of the stage.
Scene 3 returns to the garden and Ublob's spacecraft.

Costumes
Helen, Edward, Mum and the **First, Second** and **Third Children** can wear everyday clothes. **Dad** could wear a jacket and tie, or working clothes. Costuming **Ublob** could be great fun! A space suit can be created from silver survival blankets or silver lycra-type material. Wellington boots and a hat could be sprayed silver or gold. Stage make-up can be used to colour Ublob's face. The illustrations will give some ideas, and children could also be asked to draw pictures of Ublob so that you can base his costume and appearance on these.

Props
Three apples for **Edward**.
A back-pack for **Ublob**.
A wheely-bin (optional).
A whirligig clothesline (optional).
Tables and chairs.
Some kitchen utensils.
A photograph album.
A selection of foods as mentioned in the text.
A knife and fork.
A plastic cup and straw.
An ice-cube tray – with ice-cubes if possible.

30

Sound Effects
The noise of Ublob's spacecraft could be created live using a synthesiser. If you prefer a recorded effect, there is a BBC sound effects recording of 'space sounds' available from record shops and libraries.

each child recalling what has been said, in the correct order, before adding his or her own favourite food to the list.

Art
Invite the children to draw or paint pictures of Ublob's planet.

Follow-up Work

Drama
Improvisation
What would happen if Ublob visited Edward and Helen's school? Divide the class into smaller groups and ask them to create an improvisation based on this idea. Give them time to plan and rehearse their ideas before sharing them with the whole class.

Drama Games
Descriptions
Group the children in pairs. One child from each pair has to describe an object to the other. The describer is not allowed to say the name of the object, but must describe it as quickly as possible. The other child then has to guess what the object is. This can also be played as a team game, with the teacher telling one child from each team the name of an object, which the child then has to describe to the rest of the team.
I Like...
This is a memory game. Sit the class in a circle. One person begins with the words "I like eating...". He or she then has to name a favourite food; for example, "I like eating honey." The next person then has to say "I like eating honey and...", naming his or her own favourite food. ("I like eating honey and chips.") This continues with

31